D1005651

KIMUM
RIDE

MAXIMUM RIDE

MAXIMUM
RIDE
CHAPTER 1

WHUMP!

ACK!

I'LL POUR JUICE.

WOBBLE

WHO MOVED THE TABLE NEXT TO THE STAIRS?!

WOBBLE

SORRY, IGGY.

THE STAIRCASE JUST LOOKED SO EMPTY.

DON'T FORGET I'M BLIND.

THEN PLEASE ACT LIKE YOU ARE.

FLOP

RUMMAGE RUMMAGE

UMM... WISH THE FOOD FAIRIES HAD COME...

FANG!! WILL YOU QUIT THAT?!

QUIT WHAT? BREATHING?

I'LL MAKE EGGS.

MAKE SOME NOISE WHEN YOU MOVE! YOU STARTLED ME!

Huh? Fang, when did you get up??

WOBBLE

I DON'T WANT MAX TO BURN OUR LAST FRYING PAN.

......

FINE. I'LL GO GET NUDGE AND ANGEL.

......

HI, MAX.

SMILE♥

HEY, YOU'VE ALREADY DRESSED.

CAN YOU DO MY BUTTONS?

ERASERS!!

MAX...

......

THEY HAD A CHOPPER! AND GUNS! WE'RE NOT BULLET-PROOF!!

MAX?

AH...

I'M OKAY...

WHERE'S ANGEL?

ARE YOU UP, MAX?

YEAH...

....

THEY TOOK HER.

SHE'S GONE.

YOU IDIOT!

WHY DIDN'T YOU FOLLOW THEM?!!

ANGEL...

SO...THAT MAKES ME THINK WE HAVE TO GO AFTER ANGEL AGAIN.

BUT THEY WERE IN A CHOPPER. THEY'RE WAY GONE. THEY COULD BE ANYWHERE.

LIKE, CHINA OR SOMETHING...

I DON'T THINK THEY TOOK HER TO CHINA, GAZZY...

WE KNOW EXACTLY WHERE THEY TOOK HER.

WHERE'S THAT?

THE SCHOOL.

THEY TOOK ANGEL BACK TO THE SCHOOL?!

I...THINK SO.

...BUT **WE'D** END UP IN A ZOO.

WELL, WHAT ARE WE GONNA DO, THEN?

FANG, WHERE ARE YOU GOING?

WHAT IS THAT?

EEW. IT STINKS.

SHAKE

SHAKE

NEW NEW
AND WINGS
AND NEW NEW
WINGS GIRL
NEW

MUMBLE

......!!

SHAKE SHAKE

MAX... GAZZY...I'M SCARED.

WHAT HAPPENED TO MAX AND THE OTHERS? ARE THEY IN CAGES TOO?

KA

CLANG

OH MY GOD... HARRISON WAS RIGHT.

THEY GOT HER! DO YOU KNOW HOW LONG I'VE WANTED TO GET MY HANDS ON THIS ONE?

DID YOU EVER READ THE DIRECTOR'S PRECEPT REPORT ABOUT THIS RECOMBINANT GROUP?

YEAH, BUT I WASN'T SURE I BELIEVED IT.

MAXIMUM
RIDE
CHAPTER 3

WHAAAT?

OH...

...YEAH.

WE HAVE TO GO GET ANGEL BACK. WE CAN'T LET HER STAY THERE— WITH THEM.

GRAB...

THEY'RE— MONSTERS. THEY'RE GOING TO DO BAD THINGS TO HER.

AND PUT HER IN A CAGE. HURT HER.

BUT THERE'S FIVE OF US.

SO THE REST OF US HAVE TO GO GET...

Ssk...

......

NOD

HOW FAR...

NUDGE ...

...CALM DOWN.

...IS IT?

SIX HUNDRED MILES, MORE OR LESS.

WHICH MEANS AT LEAST...

...A SEVEN-HOUR FLIGHT, NOT INCLUDING BREAKS.

NO USE DISCUSSING THIS.

WE'RE WAY OUTNUMBERED.

YOU ARE SO FULL OF IT.

THAT'S NOT WHY YOU WANT US HERE.

WHY DON'T YOU JUST SAY IT?

......

OKAY.

IT'S TRUE.

I DON'T WANT YOU TO COME.

THE FACT IS, YOU'RE *BLIND*, AND WHILE YOU'RE A GREAT FLYER AROUND HERE WHERE YOU KNOW EVERYTHING...

...I CAN'T BE WORRYING ABOUT YOU IN THE MIDDLE OF A FIGHT WITH THE ERASERS.

WHAT?!!

HOLD ON!

WHAT ABOUT ME?

I DON'T CARE IF THEY HAVE GUNS AND A CHOPPER!

MAYBE NOT...

...BUT WE'LL NEVER KNOW.

JEB'S DEAD.

NOW...

...EVERYONE, GET YOUR GEAR TOGETHER.

SO, IN CASE OF EMERGENCY...

...WE ALL CLEAR ON PLAN "B," RIGHT?

UH-HUH!

IF WE GET SEPARATED SOMEHOW—

THOUGH I DON'T SEE HOW WE COULD, UNLESS MAYBE ONE OF US GETS LOST IN A CLOUD...

BABBLE

...OR SOMETHING— DO YOU THINK THAT COULD HAPPEN?

BABBLE BABBLE

I HAVEN'T EVER BEEN INSIDE A CLOUD. I BET IT'S TICKLY.

CAN YOU SEE ANYTHING INSIDE A CLOUD—

WE MEET UP AT THE NORTHMOST POINT OF LAKE MEAD.

RIGHT.

AND WHERE'S THE SCHOOL?

IN DEATH VALLEY, EIGHT MILES DUE NORTH FROM THE BADWATER BASIN.

ANYWAY, I WAS THINKING, NONE OF US EVER KNEW OUR REAL PARENTS, AND, YOU KNOW, WE'VE ALWAYS WONDERED...

...OR AT LEAST I MEAN I'VE ALWAYS WONDERED, BUT I GUESS THE REST OF YOU HAVE TOO, LIKE, WHETHER THEY GAVE US UP VOLUNTARILY OR WHETHER—

NUDGE, I KNOW HOW YOU FEEL.

BUT THOSE NAMES MIGHT NOT HAVE ANYTHING TO DO WITH YOU.

PLEASE, LET'S FOCUS ON RESCUING ANGEL.

......

MAX THOUGHT I WOULD GET IN THE WAY, JUST 'COS I'M YOUNG!!

-:HUFF:-

-:HUFF:-

......

YOU THINK THE ERASERS WILL COME BACK HERE? LIKE, THEY SAW ALL THE REST OF US. WHY WOULDN'T THEY COME BACK FOR US?

HUH.

'COURSE, IT WOULD BE HARD TO FIND THIS PLACE, AND EVEN HARDER TO GET TO IT.

NOT IF THEY HAVE A CHOPPER!

HUH. THAT'S TRUE.

WE CAN'T JUST SIT HERE AND WAIT FOR THE ERASERS TO GET US!

WE'RE SMART! WE'RE TOUGH AS NAILS! MAX MIGHT NOT HAVE THOUGHT ABOUT KEEPING THE CAMP SAFE, BUT WE DID, AND WE CAN DO IT!

YEAH, I SEE WHAT YOU MEAN.

UHHH... BUT HOW?

SHOOT!!

WE CAN MAKE TRAPS! DO SABOTAGE!

MAKE BOMBS!!

MAX? I'M STARVING!

I COULD EVEN EAT THAT UGLY BIRD!

HANG IN THERE, NUDGE.

Although that really is an ugly bird...

IT'S A TOWN.

OKAY...

MAX!

93

TAP

SO, WHAT HAVE YOU GOT TO SAY FOR YOURSELF?

SSK

IS THERE ANY REASON I SHOULDN'T TEACH YOU A LESSON TOO?

WITH MY WINGS FOLDED LIKE THIS...

...I SHOULD LOOK PERFECTLY NORMAL.

DUCK

I CAN'T
FLY IN
FRONT OF
THEM!!

MAXIMUM
RIDE

WHAT HAPPENED, REILLY?!

PANT PANT

WHAT'S GOING ON HERE?!!

IT BIT REILLY'S HAND AND HE HIT IT!!

DON'T YOU REALIZE HOW UNIQUE THIS "SUBJECT" IS?

THIS IS SUBJECT ELEVEN. DON'T YOU KNOW HOW LONG WE'VE BEEN LOOKING FOR IT? DO NOT DAMAGE THE MERCHANDISE!

I'M NOT A SUBJECT! AND I'M NOT MERCHANDISE EITHER!!

I'M SORRY.

GO TREAT YOUR HAND.

I'LL TAKE OVER HERE.

TAP

115

GOD, IT'S SO GOOD.

SO WHERE'S MAX? WHY'D SHE GO DOWN THERE?

SHE SAW SOMEONE IN TROUBLE DOWN BELOW AND WENT TO HELP.

HMMM, THAT DOES SOUND LIKE MAX.

UH...

FANG?

?

...AND BIG BOY'S DONE!

IT WON'T GO OFF TILL I SET THE TIMER. IT'S, LIKE, A SAFETY BOMB.

DO WE HAVE THE NAILS, TARP, AND COOKING OIL?

CHECK, CHECK, AND CHECK.

IT'S NIGHT OUTSIDE, SO I FOUND SOME DARK CLOTHES.

HERE YOU GO.

OKAY! NOW WE NEED TO FLY OUT, STAY OUT OF SIGHT, AND CHECK ON HOW THE ROADS RUN AND WHETHER THE ERASERS HAVE MADE CAMP ANYWHERE.

THEN WE CAN SEED THE ROADS WITH THE NAILS AND SET UP THE TARP AND OIL.

YEAH! WE ARE GENIUSES. THIS IS SUCH A GREAT PLAN!

THE HUMMER'S COMING.

NEVER KNEW THIS ABANDONED CABIN WOULD HAVE SUCH A PERFECT VIEW OF THE ROAD!!

AND THEY'RE DRIVING WAY TOO FAST.

YEAH, CAN YOU SEE IT THAT WELL?

WHOA, THAT WAS INCRED-IBLE!

I HEARD THE EXPLOSION! NOW GIVE ME THE PICTURE!

WE TOTALLY CRUSHED THEM!

WHAT HAPPENED?

ONE FELL OFF THE CLIFF AND GOT SMASHED.

THEN ANY POINT IN DROPPING BIG BOY ON THEM RIGHT NOW?

THE OTHER TWO JUST CRASHED INTO EACH OTHER. THE ERASERS ARE WALKING, SO THEY'RE NOT THAT HURT.

I DON'T THINK SO.

THEY'RE HEADING STRAIGHT INTO THE WOODS. WE'D PROBABLY CAUSE A HUGE FOREST FIRE OR SOMETHING.

ON THREE.

ONE.

TWO.

WHAT?

THREE!!

TAP

IGGY!!

GASSER! MOVE!!

DO YOU WANT TO TRY TO RUN? WHO KNOWS, YOU MIGHT GET LUCKY... FOR A LITTLE WHILE!

TAP!

...AND MAX STILL ISN'T HERE.

YOU THINK SHE'S OKAY?

NUDGE, WE NEED TO REST.

YEAH...

......

...FANG?

WHAT?

THESE
BIRDS...

...NIGHT, NUDGE.

...NIGHT, FANG...

MAXIMUM
RIDE
CHAPTER 5

146

DON'T WORRY ABOUT THE CHAIR. JUST SIT HERE AND RELAX.

......

WHY DIDN'T YOU GO TO A HOSPITAL? ...I TAKE IT YOU DON'T WANT ME TO CALL YOUR PARENTS?

......

OR THE POLICE, EITHER, RIGHT?

......

NOD

SMILE

I'M A VET, SO LET ME TAKE A LOOK AT YOUR WOUND.

ALL RIGHT...

LET'S GO TO THE BATHROOM.

GOOD MORNING, MAX. HOW ARE YOU FEELING?

I—

I'M GOOD, THANK YOU.

I'M ALL DONE AND OFF TO SCHOOL!

SEE YOU LATER!

167

HERE, HELP YOURSELF.

AND DON'T HESITATE IF YOU WANT TO TALK ABOUT... ANYTHING.

......

TH-THANKS.

IT LOOKS REALLY GOOD.

CLINK

SMILE

DO YOU HAVE A LAST NAME?

YEAH.

I GAVE IT TO MYSELF.

LIKE SALLY RIDE, THE ASTRONAUT.

MAXIMUM RIDE.

MY LAST NAME IS RIDE.

THAT'S A GOOD NAME.

......

ARE THERE OTHERS LIKE YOU?

PICK PICK

......

ERM... MAX...

...DO YOU NEED HELP?

...CAN YOU ACTUALLY FLY WITH YOUR WINGS?

WELL,
YEAH.

NOD

MY BONES
ARE...THIN.

REALLY?
YOU CAN
REALLY
FLY?

MY BONES
ARE THIN AND
LIGHT, I HAVE
EXTRA MUSCLES,
MY LUNGS ARE
BIGGER...

...AND MY HEART'S
MORE EFFICIENT.
BUT I NEED TO
EAT A LOT.

IT'S
HARD.

AH...
I SEE.

NUDGE, WHAT IF YOU MISUNDERSTOOD WHAT YOU READ AND THESE PEOPLE AREN'T RELATED TO YOU AT ALL?

EVEN IF YOU WEREN'T A TEST-TUBE BABY—WHICH YOU PROBABLY WERE—WHAT IF THERE WAS A GOOD REASON THEY GAVE YOU UP?

THEY MIGHT NOT WANT YOU BACK.

......

...DO YOU THINK...

...I HAVEN'T THOUGHT OF THAT?

I KNOW THAT! BUT I HAVE TO TRY!

I MEAN, IF THERE WAS THE SLIGHTEST CHANCE— WOULDN'T YOU TRY?

......

...I DON'T KNOW.

ZIINNG...

HI, DR. MARTINEZ.

THIS IS A FRIEND OF ELLA'S.

SHE'S DOING A REPORT ON BEING A VET, SO I'M GIVING HER A QUICK TOUR.

SURE THING.

SHUDDER!!

BA-DUMP

BA-DUMP

BA-DUMP

WHAT'S GOING ON HERE?

SORRY, MA'AM.

DOCTOR!

SORRY, DOCTOR.

FORGIVE US FOR INTERRUPTING. THERE'S NOTHING TO WORRY ABOUT. WE'RE WITH THE LOCAL AUTHORITIES.

WE'RE LOOKING FOR ANYTHING UNUSUAL...

UNUSUAL LIKE WHAT? SUGAR-FREE SODA THAT ACTUALLY TASTES GOOD?

NO. UNUSUAL PEOPLE, FOR INSTANCE. A STRANGER IN THE NEIGH-BORHOOD.

CHILDREN OR TEENAGERS YOU DON'T KNOW OR WHO LOOK SUSPICIOUS. OR UNUSUAL ANIMALS, EVEN.

I'M A VETERINARY SURGEON. I USU-ALLY DON'T LOOK AT MY PATIENTS' OWNERS MUCH, AND I HAVEN'T SEEN ANY STRANGERS AROUND.

AS FAR AS UNUSUAL ANIMALS, LAST WEEK I TREATED A COW THAT HAD A BICORNUATE UTERUS. SHE HAD A HEALTHY CALF ON EACH SIDE.

FANG...

...YOU REALLY THINK EVERYONE'S DEAD?

HERE WE GO! FRESH-BAKED CHOCOLATE-CHIP COOKIES!

WOW!

THEY SMELL SO GOOD! ♡

HOOOOOT

HAHAHA

YOU'D THINK YOU'D NEVER TASTED HOME-MADE COOKIES BEFORE.

HAVEN'T.

REALLY?

NO...THIS TASTES LIKE HEAVEN.

......

TAKE THESE WITH YOU ON YOUR WAY HOME.

THANK YOU.

W-WAIT! WHAT'S GOING ON?!

I THINK IT'S TIME FOR ME TO TAKE OFF.

NO! CAN'T YOU STAY LONGER? I LOVE HAVING YOU HERE. YOU'RE LIKE... MY SISTER!

SISTER...

...NO. PEOPLE ARE DEPENDING ON ME.

WILL YOU EVER COME BACK TO VISIT?

......

......

...PROBABLY NOT...

MAX, TAKE THIS BAG.

N-NO, IT'S OKAY.

PLEASE TAKE IT. IT'S AN OLD ONE— I DON'T USE IT ANYMORE. AND...I PUT MY PHONE NUMBER INSIDE.

IF YOU EVER NEED ANYTHING, ANYTHING AT ALL, PLEASE CALL US. I ALSO PUT SOME MONEY IN, JUST IN CASE.

AH... BUT...

IT'S NOT MUCH, SO PLEASE TAKE IT WITH YOU. I JUST... FEEL LIKE YOU'RE A DAUGHTER TO ME.

......

THANK YOU...

...THEY ACCEPTED ME FOR WHO I AM. IF THEY WERE MY FAMILY...

MAXIMUM RIDE
CHAPTER 7

FANG... NUDGE...

DID THEY EVER MAKE IT HERE? WHAT IF —

MAX!

NUDGE!

MAX! MAX! I CAN'T BELIEVE IT! CAN I BELIEVE IT?

LET'S GO BACK TO THE CAVE AND TALK.

NO...

WAS IT... WAS IT AFTER THE OIL-SLICK HUMMER CRASH?

OIL-SLICK HUMMER CRASH?!

YOU GUYS SET OFF A BOMB? DIDN'T THAT TELL THE ERASERS EXACTLY WHERE YOU WERE?

YOU SHOULD HAVE STAYED HIDDEN!

BUT THEY ALREADY KNEW WHERE WE WERE!

THEY'D SEEN ALL OF US— THEY KNEW WE WERE IN THE AREA.

OR MAYBE IT WAS... AFTER THE BOMB.

NOD

I THINK IT WAS THE BOMB. THAT DEFINITELY SEEMED TO TICK THEM OFF.

BOMB ?!

......!!

THERE'S A MICROCHIP IN YOUR FORE-ARM.

WELL, I'M GLAD YOU'RE SAFE.

HOW WERE YOU GUYS, FANG AND NUDGE?

SORRY TO KEEP YOU WAITING...

I...TRIED TO FIND MY MOM FROM THE ADDRESS I SAW IN THE FILES.

WHAAAT? YOUR MOM?

BUT THE ERASERS, INCLUDING THAT DIRTBAG ARI, SHOWED UP AND GAVE FANG A HARD TIME.

SO YOU DIDN'T TALK TO HER? DID SHE LOOK NICE?

...UM...

...I'LL TELL YOU ABOUT IT LATER.

AH...

WE'VE LEARNED SOME STUFF FROM THE HAWKS.

SHRUG

Went that bad, huh?

SOME BANKING MOVES, HOW THEY COMMU-NICATE, STUFF LIKE THAT.

HAWKS ARE REALLY COOL.

CAN YOU TEACH US WHAT YOU LEARNED?

RIGHT! THEY, LIKE, USE THE TIPS OF THEIR FEATHERS TO HELP THEM AIM, AND WE TRIED IT, AND IT WAS AMAZING. A LITTLE THING LIKE THAT MAKES SUCH A DIFFERENCE.

YEAH, SURE.

NOD

AND I DON'T KNOW IF ANY OF YOU HAVE ONE...

...THERE MIGHT NOT BE ANY "SAFE ZONE" FOR US.

BUT WE CAN'T TURN BACK NOW.

NO MATTER WHAT...

...WE'RE GOING AFTER ANGEL.

MAX, I'M STARVING.

WE HAVEN'T EATEN ANYTHING SINCE THOSE CHOCOLATE-CHIP COOKIES...

YAAAAY!!

I WANT MY ROOM TO SMELL JUST LIKE THIS.

LET'S ALL EAT!

I DON'T EAT MEAT ANYMORE, SO YOU CAN HAVE THIS.

MUNCH MUNCH

SLURP SLURP

SO YUMMY!

IT WOULD BE NICE TO TAKE OUR TIME, BUT WE DON'T KNOW WHEN THE ERASERS WILL SHOW UP.

LET'S HURRY AND FINISH OUR MEAL SO WE CAN LEAVE RIGHT AWAY.

ESPECIALLY IF THERE REALLY IS A MICROCHIP IN MY ARM.

OKAY!

......

ELLA...

DR. MARTINEZ...

BOLT

FANG...

NOD

PEEK...

NUDGE

DON'T LOOK UP. IN THREE SECONDS ...

...JUMP OVER FANG AND OUT THAT EXIT DOOR.

SLURP

TAP

BOLT

DAMN IT, THEY'RE OUT HERE TOO! LOOK OUT!

MAXIMUM RIDE.

OH, I'VE MISSED YOU SO MUCH.

I'M HALLUCINATING.

I KNOW YOU'RE SURPRISED.

THIS MAN, JEB, HAD KIDNAPPED THE SIX OF US FOUR YEARS AGO, STOLEN US FROM THIS FREAK SHOW.

CLATTER

I'LL GET US SOME HOT CHOCOLATE.

I KNOW IT'S YOUR FAVORITE.

HE HID US IN THE MOUNTAINS AND FED AND CLOTHED US LIKE A PARENT. HE TAUGHT US SURVIVAL SKLLS, HOW TO FIGHT, AND HOW TO READ.

WE FOLLOWED HIM LIKE A PARENT TOO, AND HE HAD BEEN OUR ONE AND ONLY COMFORT.

YEN+

HERE YOU GO, MAX.

TAP

...YOU ARE SUPPOSED TO **SAVE THE WORLD.**

To be continued in MAXIMUM RIDE, Vol. 2!

♡ Afterword from NaRae Lee ♡

MY AFTERWORD FOR CHAPTER SEVEN AND THE COLLECTED BOOK!

WOW~ I CAN'T BELIEVE THE FIRST VOLUME OF THE BOOK IS ALREADY DONE!!

Hair already growing out (messy)

WHEN MY EDITOR FIRST ASKED ME TO WORK ON MAXIMUM RIDE, I DIDN'T KNOW IT WAS THIS HUGE A PROJECT. T.T I DIDN'T REALLY HAVE MUCH TIME TO THINK, BUT I THOUGHT IT WAS A GREAT OPPORTUNITY AND STARTED ON IT...I NEVER THOUGHT I WOULD BE PUBLISHED FAR AWAY IN AMERICA! (ESPECIALLY ON A BESTSELLER TITLE!!)

SO IT'S SIMPLE. YOU JUST HAVE TO DRAW FOR AN AMERICAN MAGAZINE.

????

HUH?! AMERICA?!

ONLY AFTER I MET THE DIRECTOR DID I ACTUALLY REALIZE THAT I WAS WORKING WITH AN AMERICAN PUBLISHER. BEFORE THAT, SINCE IT WAS SO OUT OF THE BLUE, I THOUGHT MY EDITOR MIGHT JUST BE JOKING WITH ME. (LOL)

ABCDEFG

The director who I now can't remember that clearly. T.T

GAH~! HE'S A REAL FOREIGNER!

AND THEN BEFORE I REALIZED IT, THE SERIALIZATION HAD STARTED AND I WAS WORKING ON MAXIMUM RIDE.

I TOLD THE DIRECTOR THAT I WOULD PRACTICE MY ENGLISH BEFORE I MET HIM AGAIN...

Too hard!

...BUT I HAVE BEEN SO BUSY THAT NOT ONLY DID I NOT LEARN ENGLISH, BUT I ALSO FORGOT THE JAPANESE I HAD LEARNED... T.T

BUT I STILL REMEMBER HIM SAYING, "YOU'RE MORE ATTRACTIVE 'COS YOU DON'T SPEAK ENGLISH. MORE EXOTIC." (I'M ATTRACTIVE!!)

<< THE DESK I WORK ON. THIS IS MY ROOM AT MY PARENTS' HOUSE. I USE THE COMPUTER TO DO THE TONING OR TO WORK ON PROJECTS OTHER THAN MAXIMUM RIDE.

I USED TO PENCIL A LOT AT A NEARBY CAFÉ. IT CAN GET A LITTLE STUFFY IF YOU STAY HOME FOR TOO LONG...

ESPECIALLY IN THE SUMMER, I WENT TO ENJOY THE COOL ICED COFFEE AND THE AIR CONDITIONING!!

AND FOR THE INKING, I MOSTLY WORK AT MY BACKGROUND ASSISTANT FRIEND'S HOUSE. WE GO TO THE SAME SCHOOL NOW AND ALSO WENT TO THE SAME HIGH SCHOOL, SO IT'S COMFY AND NICE. (IS IT JUST COMFY FOR ME?!)

BY THE TIME I START ON THE SECOND VOLUME I WILL HAVE MY OWN STUDIO!

Go work at your own house!

COME HOME!! → Mom.

EVERY TIME THE DEADLINE GOT CLOSE, SOMETHING WOULD BREAK... (THE MONITOR, THE KEYBOARD, AND MY CELL PHONE WAS EVEN OUT OF ORDER TILL NOW... RECENTLY, MY HARD DRIVE SEEMS TO BE ILL TOO, SO I'M WORRIED...)

...OR THIS AND THAT WOULD HAPPEN TO ME PERSONALLY (EVERY TIME, EITHER ME OR MY ASSISTANT WOULD GET SICK) MAKING IT HARDER TO MEET THE DEADLINE.

COUGH COUGH

BUT I'M HAPPY I STILL MANAGED TO COME THIS FAR, TO HAVE THIS HEAVY NUMBER OF PAGES.

IT'S ALL THANKS TO MY EDITOR'S KIND SUPPORT AND PRAISE.

THEY SAY COMPLIMENTS WILL MAKE EVEN A WHALE DANCE! THANK YOU SO MUCH, MY EDITOR! VISIT KOREA SOON. ^^

total 240p?

IN ADDITION TO MAXIMUM RIDE, I STARTED A NEW SERIES IN KOREA AS WELL. IT IS A TITLE FOR LITTLE GIRLS CALLED SWEETIE MILKY PROPOSAL. (I THINK AMERICANS MIGHT LAUGH AT THE TITLE... T.T;;)

IT'S VERY DIFFERENT FROM MAXIMUM RIDE.

IT'S EIGHT PAGES A MONTH... I HOPE IT GOES WELL, AND SOMEDAY I WILL GET TO SHOW IT TO THE AMERICAN READERS TOO. ^^

ANYWAY, IT'S ALREADY
BEEN TEN MONTHS SINCE I STARTED
WORKING ON MAXIMUM RIDE!! I REALLY FELL
IN LOVE WITH THE SIX MAIN CHARACTERS!
(SOMETIMES I FEEL LIKE THEY'RE MY OWN
LITTLE BROTHERS AND SISTERS.)

SOMETIMES WHEN I'M WORKING
HARD, MAX AND THE FLOCK APPEAR IN MY
DREAMS AND WE ALL FLY TOGETHER! (LOL)

NO TIME TO
SLEEP! LET'S GO
WORK!!!

NoNo∞∞

Argh...
Don't do
this...

Why is Max
speaking in Korean
anyway??

HONESTLY...I STILL CAN'T BELIEVE
THE FACT THAT THE MAXIMUM RIDE I DREW
IS SELLING IN A LAND MUCH LARGER THAN
KOREA. (IT DOESN'T HELP THAT I NEVER GOT
TO ACTUALLY SEE IT IN STORES. T.T)
IT STILL FEELS LIKE A DREAM!!

It's even
in stores
here!!

Friend who lives
in Canada

I WANT TO SEE MY
BOOK IN BOOKSTORES
TOO. SOB-SOB...

I KNOW I HAVE A
LOT TO LEARN, BUT I
HOPE YOU KEEP ENJOYING
MAXIMUM RIDE!!

IF YOU CAN READ KOREAN
OR YOU WANT TO SEE MORE OF MY ART,
PLEASE COME AND VISIT MY BLOG!

HTTP://BLOG.NAVER.COM/NARE870815

I WANT TO SEND MY SPECIAL THANKS TO
JUYOUN LEE, MY EDITOR, MOONJU, WHO HELPED
ME WITH THE BACKGROUNDS, DONGWOO, WHO
HELPED ME WITH ERASING AND THE INKS, MY
MOTHER, WHO ALWAYS WORRIES ABOUT MY
HEALTH, AND LASTLY ALL THE PROFESSORS AT
CHUNGKANG UNIVERSITY.

THANK YOU SO, SO MUCH!!

Read on to enjoy a sneak
preview of MAX,
the flock's latest adventure
from best-selling
author James Patterson.

JAMES PATTERSON

MAX

Maximum Ride

PROLOGUE
The Madness
Never Stops

Near Los Angeles Basin, California

There.

Devin raised his right arm and focused directly over his wrist. It took less than a millisecond to calculate the trajectory — he didn't have a built-in computer, but his 220 IQ served him well.

He slowly breathed in and out, getting ready to squeeze the trigger between breaths, between heartbeats. His sensitive nose wrinkled as the ever-present smog that hovered over the Los Angeles Basin filled his lungs. He hated to think what the pollutants were doing to his brain cells but accepted that some things were necessary evils.

There.

His light eyes expertly tracked the objects flying overhead: one, two, three, four, five, six. Seven? There was a small seventh object, unexpected but quickly determined to be unimportant. Actually, all of them were unimportant. All but one. The one in front.

He knew they had raptor vision. He merely had extraordinary eyesight. It was good enough. All the same, the crosshairs in the gun sight attached to his wrist made missing an impossibility. He never missed.

That's why they saved him for extraspecial missions like this one.

Many, many others had already failed at this task. Devin felt utter disdain for them. To kill one bird kid — how hard could it be? They were flesh and blood, ridiculously fragile. It wasn't like bullets bounced off them.

Once more Devin raised his arm and observed his prey, catching her neatly in the crosshairs, as if they could pin her to the sky. The flock flew, perfectly spaced, in a large arc overhead, the one called Maximum in front, flanked by the two large males. Then a smaller female. Then a smaller male, and the smallest female.

A little black object, not bird kid shaped, struggled to keep up. Devin couldn't identify it — it hadn't been in his dossier. The closest thing he could imagine was if someone grafted wings onto a small dog or something, as unlikely as that was.

But Max was the only one he was concerned with. It was Max he was supposed to kill, Max whom he kept catching in his sights.

Devin sighed and lowered his arm. This was almost too easy. It wasn't sporting. He loved the chase, the hunt, the split-second intersection of luck and skill that allowed him to exercise his perfection, his inability to miss.

He looked down at what used to be his right hand. One could get used to having no right hand. It was surprisingly easy. And it was so superior to have this lovely weapon instead.

It wasn't as crude as simply having a Glock 18 grafted to the stump of an amputated limb. It was so much more elegant than that, so much more a miracle of design and ingenuity. This weapon was a part of him physically, responsive to his slightest thought, triggered by almost imperceptible nerve firings in the interface between his arm and the weapon.

He was a living work of art. Unlike the bird kids flying in traceable patterns overhead.

Devin had seen the posters, the advertisements. Those naive, do-gooder idiots at the Coalition to Stop the Madness had organized this whole thing, this air show, this demonstration of supposedly "evolved" humans.

Wrong. The bird kids were ill-conceived accidents. He, Devin, was truly an evolved human.

The CSM zealots were wasting their time — and everyone else's. Using the bird kids to promote their own agenda was a typically selfish, shortsighted thing to do. Manipulating and taking advantage of lesser creatures in order to "save" even lesser creatures? It was a joke.

A joke that could not be perpetrated without this flock of examples. And the flock could not survive without its leader.

Once again Devin raised his arm and closed his left eye to focus through the gun sight on his wrist. He angled the Glock a millimeter to the left and smoothly tracked his target as she arced across the sky.

One breath in, one breath out. One heartbeat, two heartbeats, and here we go . . .

PART 1

Freaks and M-Geeks

1

"And a-one, and a-two —" Nudge said, leaning into a perfect forty-five-degree angle. Her tawny russet wings glowed warmly in the afternoon sunlight.

Behind her, the Gasman made squealing-brakes sounds as he dropped his feet down and slowed drastically. "Hey! Watch gravity in action!" he yelled, folding his wings back to create an unaerodynamic eight-year-old, his blond hair blown straight up by the wind.

I rolled my eyes. "Gazzy, stick to the choreography!" He was sinking fast, and I had to bellow to make sure he heard me. "This is a paying job! Don't blow it!" Okay, they were paying us mostly in doughnuts, but let's not quibble.

Even from this high up, I could hear the exclamations of surprise, the indrawn gasps that told me our captive audience below had noticed one of us dropping like a rock.

I'd give him five seconds, and then I'd swoop down after him. One . . . two . . .

I wasn't sure about this whole air-show thing to begin with, but how could I refuse my own mom? After our last "working vacation" in Ant-freaking-arctica, my mom and a bunch of scientists had created an organization called the Coalition to Stop the Madness, or CSM. Basically, they were trying to tell the whole world about the dangers of pollution, greenhouse gases, dependence on foreign oil — you get the picture.

Already, more than a thousand scientists, teachers, senators, and regular people had joined the CSM. One of the teacher-members had come up with the traveling air-show idea to really get the message out. I mean, Blue Angels, Schmue Angels, but flying mutant bird kids? Come on! Who's gonna pass that up?

So here we were, flying perfect formations, doing tricks, air dancing, la la la, the six of us and Total, whose wings by now had pretty much finished developing. He could fly, at least, but he wasn't exactly Baryshnikov. If Baryshnikov had been a small, black, Scottie dog with wings, that is.

By the time I'd counted to four, the Gasman had ended his free fall and was soaring upward again, happiness on his relatively clean face.

Hanging out with the CSM folks had some benefits, chiefly food and decent places to sleep. And, of course, seeing my mom, which I'd never be able to get enough of, after living the first fourteen years of my life not even knowing she existed. (I explained all this in earlier books, if you want to go get caught up.)

"Yo," said Fang, hovering next to me.

My heart gave a little kick as I saw how the sun glinted off his deeply black feathers. Which matched his eyes. And his hair. "You enjoying being a spokesfreak?" I asked him casually, looking away.

One side of his mouth moved: the Fang version of unbridled chortling.

He shrugged. "It's a job."

"Yep. So long as they don't worry about pesky child-labor laws," I agreed. We're an odd little band, my fellow flock members and I. Fang, Iggy, and I are all fourteen, give or take. So officially, technically, legally, we're minors. But we've been living on our own for years, and regular child-protection laws just don't seem to apply to us. Come to think of it, many regular grown-up laws don't seem to apply to us either.

Nudge is eleven, roughly. The Gasman is eightish. Angel is somewhere in the six range. I don't know how old Total is, and frankly, what with the calculations of dog years into human years, I don't care.

Suddenly, out of nowhere, Angel dropped down onto me with all her forty-one pounds of feathery fun.

"Oof! What are you doing, goofball?" I exclaimed, dipping about a foot. Then I heard it: the high-pitched, all-too-familiar whine of a bullet streaking past my ear, close enough to knock some of my hair aside.

In the next second, Total yelped piercingly, spinning in midair, his small black wings flapping frantically. Angel's quick instincts had saved my life. But Total had taken the hit.

2

In the blink of an eye, I rolled a full 360, spinning in the air, swooping to catch Total and also performing evasive maneuvers that, sadly, I've had way too much practice doing.

"Scatter!" I shouted. "Get out of firing range!"

We all peeled away, our wings moving fast and powerfully, gaining altitude like rockets. I heard applause floating up to me — they thought this was part of the act. Then I looked down at the limp black dog in my arms.

"Total!" I said, holding his chunky little body. "Total!"

He blinked and moaned. "I'm hit, Max. They got me. I guess I'm gonna live fast, die young, and leave a beautiful corpse, huh?"

Okay. In my experience, if you're really hit or seriously hurt, you don't say much. Maybe a few bad words. Maybe grunting sounds. You don't manage pithy quotes.

Quickly I shifted him this way and that, scanning for wounds. He had both ears, and his face was fine. I patted along his wings, which still looked too short to keep him aloft. Bright red blood stained my sleeve, but so far he seemed to be in one unperforated piece.

"Tell Akila," Total gasped, eyelids fluttering, "tell her she's always been the only one." Akila is the Alaskan Malamute Total had fallen for back on the Wendy K., the boat where we lived with a bunch of scientists on our way to Antarctica.

"Shh," I said. "I'm still looking for holes."

"I don't have many regrets," Total rambled weakly. "True, I thought about a career in the theater, once our adventures waned. I know it's just a crazy dream, but I always hoped for just one chance to play the Dane before I died."

"Play the huh?" I said absently, feeling his ribs. Nothing broken. "Is that a game?"

Total moaned and closed his eyes.

Then I found it: the source of the blood, the place where he'd been shot.

"Total?" I said, and got a slight whimper. "You have a boo-boo on your tail."

"What?" He opened his eyes and curled to peer at his short tail. He wagged it experimentally, outrage appearing on his face as he realized a tiny chunk of flesh was missing near the tip. "I'm hit! I'm bleeding! Those scoundrels will pay for this!"

"I think a Band-Aid is probably all you need." I struggled to keep a straight face.

Fang swerved closer to me, big and supremely graceful, like a black panther with wings.

Oh, God. I'm so stupid. Forget I just said that.

"How's he doing?' Fang asked, nodding at Total.

"He needs a Band-Aid," I said. A look passed between me and Fang, full of suppressed humor, relief, understanding, love —

Forget I said that too. I don't know what's wrong with me.

"Got your sniper," Fang went on, pointing downward.

I shifted into battle mode. "One sniper or a whole flotilla of baddies?"

"Only see the one."

I raised an eyebrow. "So, what, we're not worth a whole flotilla anymore?" I looked down at Total. "Wings out, spud. You gotta fly on your own."

Total gathered himself with dignity, extended his wings, and jumped awkwardly out of my arms. He flapped frantically, then with more confidence, and rose to keep up with us.

"What's up?" Iggy had coasted on an updraft for a while, but now he and the others were forming a bird-kid sandwich around me.

"Total's okay," I reported. "One sniper below. Now we gotta go take him out."

Angel's pure-white wing brushed against me. She gave me a sweet smile that melted my heart, and I tried to remember that this kid had many layers, not all of them made of gumdrops and roses.

"Thanks, lamby," I said, and she grinned.

"I felt something bad about to happen," she explained. "Can we go get that guy now?"

"Let's do it," I said, and we angled ourselves downward. Among the many genetic enhancements we sport, the mad scientists who created us had thoughtfully included raptor vision. I raked the land below, almost a mile down, and traced the area where Fang pointed.

I saw him: a lone guy in the window of a building close to the air base. He was tracking us, and we began our evasive actions, dropping suddenly, swerving, angling different ways, trying to be as unpredictable as possible. We're fairly good at being unpredictable.

"Mass zoom?" Fang asked, and I nodded.

"Ig, mass zoom, angle down about thirty-five degrees. Then aim for six o'clock," I instructed. And why was I only giving Iggy instructions? Because Iggy's the only blind one, that's why.

We were moving fast, really fast, dropping at a trajectory that would smash us into the sniper's window in about eight seconds. We'd practiced racing feet-first through open windows a thousand times, one right after the other, bam bam bam. So this was more of a fun challenge than a scary, death-defying act of desperation.

The two things often look very similar in our world.

Seven, six, five, I counted silently.

When I got to four, the window exploded outward, knocking me head over heels.

3

Three days later . . .

Here, in no particular order, is a massively incomplete list of things that make me twitchy:

1) Being indoors, almost anywhere
2) Places with no easy exits
3) People who promise me tons of "benefits" and assume that I don't see right through the crapola to the stark truth that actually they want me to do a bunch of stuff for them
4) Being dressed up

So it won't take a lot of imagination on your part to guess how I reacted to our appointment at a Hollywood talent agency.

"Come in, guys," said the most gorgeous woman I've ever seen. She flashed glowing white teeth and tossed back her perfect, auburn hair as she ushered us through the heavy wooden door. "I'm Sharon. Welcome!"

I could see her trying to avoid looking at our various bruises, scrapes, and cuts. Well, if you're six feet away from a building when it explodes at you, you're gonna get a little banged up. Fact of life.

We were in a big office building in Hollywood. If you've been keeping up with our nutty, action-packed shenanigans, you'll remember how many incredibly bad experiences we've had inside office buildings. They're pretty much my least favorite place to be, right after dungeons and hospitals, but before dog crates and science labs. Call me quirky.

A member of the CSM had a friend who had a friend who had a cousin who was married to someone who knew someone at this huge, important Hollywood talent agency and volunteered us for an interview, without asking us. The CSM thought we spokesbirds were doing a bang-up job of getting their message out. Emphasis on bang, given the suicide sniper. But more on that later.

"Come in! Come in!" A short, balding guy in a flashy suit waved us in, big smile in place. I ratcheted up my DEFCON level to orange. "I'm Steve Blackman."

There were four of them altogether, three guys and Sharon with the great hair. She blinked when Total trotted in after us, a small white bandage still covering the tip of his tail. He'd gotten more mileage out of that weensy flesh wound than I've gotten out of broken ribs.

"Good God," I heard Total mutter as he looked at the woman. "She can't be real."

"Max!" said Steve, holding out his hand. "May I call you Max?"

"No." I frowned and looked at his hand until he pulled it back.

The other two guys introduced themselves, and we just stood there, unsmiling. Actually, Nudge smiled a little. She loves stuff like this. She'd even worn a skirt. Angel was wearing a pink tutu over her jeans. My clothes were at least clean and not blood-spattered, which is about as good as it ever gets with me.

"Well!" said Steve, rubbing his hands together. "Let's sit down and get to know each other, huh? Can we get you something to drink? You kids hungry?"

"We're always hungry," said the Gasman seriously.

Steve looked taken aback. "Ah, yes, of course! Growing kids!" He was trying hard not to look at our wings, with limited success. He reached over and tapped a button on his desk, which was so big you could practically land a chopper on it. "Jeff? How about some drinks and snacks in here? Thanks."

"Please, sit down," Sharon said, with another hair toss. I made a mental note to practice doing that in a mirror the next time I saw one. It seemed a useful skill, right up there with roundhouse kicks.

We sat, making sure no one was in back of us or could sneak up on us. I was wound so tight I was about to break out in hives.

A young guy in a purple-striped shirt came in with a tray of sodas, glasses of ice, and little nibbly things on several plates. "They're tapas," he explained. "This one's calamari, and this one's —"

"Thanks a million, Jeff." Steve cut in with a smile. Jeff straightened and left, closing the door quietly behind him. Then, as we fell on the food like hyenas, Steve turned to us again, looking so dang enthusiastic that I wondered how much coffee he'd had this morning. "So! You kids want to be big stars, eh?"

"God, no!" I said, almost spewing crumbs. "No way!"

Oddly, this seemed to throw a petite wrench into the convo.

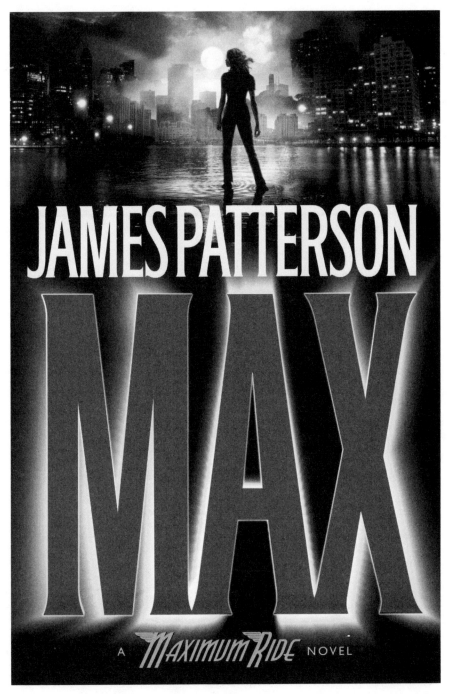

AVAILABLE MARCH 16, 2009

MAXIMUM RIDE: THE MANGA ①

JAMES PATTERSON
& NaRae Lee

Adaptation and Illustration: NaRae Lee

Lettering: Abigail Blackman

MAXIMUM RIDE, THE MANGA, Vol. 1 © 2009 by SueJack, Inc.

Illustrations © 2009 Hachette Book Group, Inc.

All rights reserved. Except as permitted under the U.S. Copyright Act of 1976, no part of this publication may be reproduced, distributed, or transmitted in any form or by any means, or stored in a database or retrieval system, without the prior written permission of the publisher.

The characters and events in this book are fictitious. Any similarity to real persons, living or dead, is coincidental and not intended by the author.

Yen Press
Hachette Book Group
237 Park Avenue, New York, NY 10017

Visit our Web sites at www.HachetteBookGroup.com and www.YenPress.com.

Yen Press is an imprint of Hachette Book Group, Inc. The Yen Press name and logo are trademarks of Hachette Book Group, Inc.

First Yen Press Edition: January 2009

ISBN-13: 978-0-7595-2951-9

10 9 8 7 6 5 4 3 2 1

BVG

Printed in the United States of America